C000163003

FIGHTING SHIPS

Antony Preston

Exeter Books

NEW YORK

Page 1: *A Sea Wolf missile launcher fitted to a Royal Navy frigate. The system underwent trials on HMS* Penelope *in 1976 and became fully operational three years later when it was fitted to HMS* Broadsword. *Sea Wolf is capable of 'splashing' incoming aircraft and missiles at ranges up to 5000 yards.*

Pages 2-3: *The USS* Enterprise *(CVN-65) was the world's first nuclear-powered aircraft carrier when she was launched in 1960. The vessel carries 86 aircraft and her defensive armament includes Sea Sparrow missiles and Phalanx CIWS guns.*

Copyright © 1989 by Brompton Books Corp

First published in USA 1989
by Exeter Books
Distributed by Bookthrift
Exeter is a trademark of Bookthrift Marketing, Inc.
Bookthrift is a registered trademark of Bookthrift
Marketing New York, New York

ALL RIGHTS RESERVED

ISBN 0-7917-0076-3

Printed in Hong Kong

Acknowledgments

Aviation Photographs International, pages 28, 43(bottom).
Beken of Cowes Ltd, pages 34-6.
Canadian Armed Forces, page 97.
Defense Miltronics, page 39.
Fleet Photographic Unit, UK, pages 22(bottom), 23, 48(bottom), 94, 115.
General Dynamics Electric Boat Division, page 9.
Mike Lennon Photographic, pages 14, 48(top), 52, 68, 73(bottom), 86, 96(bottom), 98, 110(top), 111, 117(bottom), 124.
Marine Nationale, France, page 49.
MARS/US Navy, page 75.
MGW Picture Library, pages 1, 16, 20, 22(top), 24, 25, 30-1, 61, 69, 72, 73(top), 84, 85, 87(bottom), 88-9, 96(top), 99, 102, 117(top), 122, 123(bottom), 125.
Alan Pittaway Collection, pages 24, 47, 65, 80, 90, 107, 110(bottom), 119.
Photri, pages 11, 32, 38, 43(top), 45, 55(top), 78, 123(top).
TRH, pages 13, 18-19, 21, 44, 46, 51, 55(bottom), 56, 60, 64, 74, 76, 77, 79, 81(both), 87(top), 91, 92, 93(both),/Vickers 95, 101, 103, 106, 109, 113, 114(bottom), 118, 126.
US Naval Photographic Center, pages 2-3, 11, 12, 15, 17, 27, 33, 37, 40-1, 42, 53, 54, 57, 59, 62, 63, 66, 67, 70-1, 83, 104-5, 108, 112(both), 114(top), 121.
Yarrow Shipbuilders, page 116.

CONTENTS

INTRODUCTION

At the end of World War II it was fashionable in some military circles to suggest that the growing range of aircraft, their increased sophistication and awesome weaponry would render obsolescent many of the tasks performed by the world's navies. For example, what role would amphibious transports perform when huge cargo aircraft could transport men and equipment thousands of miles in a shorter time? Today, however, nobody takes this proposition seriously. If history has taught the strategists anything over the decades since 1945, it is that warships have an invaluable role to play in geopolitics. In the defense of a nation's maritime interests, whether the protection of overseas trade or the projection of power across vast distances, naval forces are essential.

Out of all the changes that have taken place in sea warfare since the last world war, three developments stand out: the application of electronics, guided missiles and nuclear power. Collectively they have wrought great changes in the shape and role of naval vessels and, perhaps most importantly, have made a navy the most costly element in a nation's armory. Until the recent past the navies of the Western Alliance have held both the quantitative and qualitative edge over their Warsaw Pact opponents, a situation seen as being essential to NATO interests given that any effort to reinforce Western Europe from the United States in time of crisis would be borne by the navies of the member states. The numerical and technological advantages enjoyed by the West have been lost to a certain degree to the Soviet Navy under the direction of Admiral Sergei Gorshkov. While the Soviet Navy has been expanding to take on a greater global role, the naval chiefs of the West have been wrestling with the constraints imposed on them by financial cutbacks.

Although it is difficult to compare the capabilities of the world's major ship classes, a few general points can be outlined. Most have all or a combination of the following attributes: offensive and defensive weaponry, whether missiles or large-caliber guns; a sophisticated array of electronic equipment for detecting and providing the necessary information to deal with any threat; and thirdly some form of air support, from anti-submarine helicopters to the massive wings operating from the carriers of the US Navy. One of the key questions faced by naval theorists is the need to find an effective balance between the offensive and defensive weaponry carried by fighting ships.

Since the 1960s the design and cost of naval vessels have been chiefly influenced by the pressures to provide the electronics that make a vessel a truly effective fighting unit. The importance of this technology can be gauged by the simple fact that only some 10 percent of the cost of building a ship is generated by hull construction. The provision of integrated electronic systems has somewhat reduced the number of crewmen required to operate a vessel but has also increased the size of most ship types. The truth is that while the weaponry on the deck of a modern vessel may look rather simple and small scale, its vital electronics are bulky in the extreme. Few can doubt that electronics have made the modern warship a powerful fighting unit, a vessel able to deal with a threat with great precision and economy of effort.

One further aspect of postwar naval development needs considering: the impact of advances in submarine warfare. Many commentators did overstate the case for submarines to the extent of claiming that they would render all other vessels irrelevant. Nevertheless the development of nuclear-powered and nuclear-armed vessels has profoundly changed naval thinking. So potent are modern submarines that most surface vessels are designed to counter their threat, along with that of aircraft. In the realm of superpower politics, ballistic-missile armed nuclear-powered submarines are symbols of strength. Silent, difficult to track and capable of inflicting destruction on a massive scale, they perhaps more than any other vessels afloat symbolize the continuing role and strength of the modern fighting ship.

SUBMARINES

Today submarines are among the most potent warships in existence, but they are no longer cheap alternatives to surface vessels. A modern nuclear attack submarine is about three-quarters of the cost of a big cruiser, and more than twice as expensive as a missile-armed frigate.

The large size of today's nuclear submarines is the result of complex design forces. Speed calls for larger machinery, while combat systems and sonars have grown bigger to provide greater accuracy and, above all, space requirements have risen due to the need to reduce radiated noise by isolating machinery from the hull. Another size-increasing factor is the need to accommodate more weapons. For all their fighting qualities big submarines carry comparatively few weapons, and efforts are being made to increase the number of torpedoes and missiles available. Experience in two world wars showed that a submarine's operational effectiveness was limited by the number of torpedoes and missiles she carried — when they were expended she presented no threat and had to return home.

There are, of course, limits to their effectiveness. At high speed submarines are noisy, and will betray their presence if they try to attack at anything but slow speed. High speed is most useful in providing strategic mobility. Although it is possible to communicate with submerged submarines the procedure is slow, and submarines cannot match the tactical flexibility of surface warships, which can communicate freely whether ship-to-ship, ship-to-shore or ship-to-aircraft.

Non-nuclear submarines operating on electric power are inherently quieter than nuclear boats, but lack their ability to cover great distances at high speed. Many current diesel-electric submarines are intended primarily for anti-ship attack, and need only comparatively simple combat systems. However, as soon as a diesel-electric submarine is required to perform the anti-submarine or 'hunter-killer' mission the need for a more complex combat system forces size upward. Diesel-electric submarines are hard to detect but the need to recharge their batteries by snorkeling makes them vulnerable. New developments in propulsion, notably the closed-cycle Stirling engine and electrochemical fuel cells, are intended to cut the time spent snorkeling. Modern batteries can be charged more rapidly, and hold a higher charge for greater endurance.

Apart from ballistic missiles, the torpedo is the main weapon of modern submarines and is usually wire-guided and fitted with a variety of homing systems. But underwater-launched anti-ship missiles are also carried, fired from torpedo or separate vertical tubes. Mines can be laid, usually through torpedo tubes, as an alternative to torpedoes, although some boats have separate minelaying systems.

Right: *The USS Georgia (SSBN-729), one of the Ohio class of nuclear-powered ballistic-missile submarines, is the largest submarine built by any Western nation and is a member of the only 24-tube ballistic submarine class in the world. They can descend to about 1000 feet and have a cruising endurance of about 70 days.*

Above: *The USS* Lafayette, *the lead-boat in its class of nuclear-powered ballistic-missile submarines, cuts through the swell of a rough sea. The crew, some 140 men, can operate at sea for periods of up to 70 days without returning to base. The Lafayette class boats entered service in the 1960s and will reach the end of their service life in the 1990s. Displacement is 8250 tons submerged; top speed is 25 knots under water.*

Above: *The USS* Georgia *and her sisters are powered by S8G pressurized water reactors and, despite initial worries, they have proved to be the quietest power units in service with any navy. The powerplant permits a top surface speed of 28 knots; submerged the speed is two knots higher.*

Above: *The USS* Ohio *(SSBN-726), the lead-boat in its class, began its operational deployment on 1 October 1982. A member of Submarine Squadron 17, a unit established on 5 January 1981, the* Ohio *and the subsequent seven boats in the class have recently been modernized to carry Trident C-4 ballistic missiles.*

Above: *An Ohio class strategic submarine at base. Reactor design improvements have allowed a nine-year maintenance cycle to be adopted, and an overall improvement in servicing techniques have given the class a 66 percent availability. The operating schedule is 70 days at sea followed by a 25-day refit and crew change, and a 12-month overhaul every nine years.*

Above: *The USS* Bluefish, *one of the navy's Sturgeon class nuclear-powered attack submarines, was built by General Dynamics between 1968 and 1971. Like her sisters, she is driven by the Westinghouse S5W2 reactor plant which drives the 4640-ton vessel at 15 knots on the surface and at 30 knots submerged. Sturgeon class vessels have a safe maximum diving depth of 1300 feet, and operate in both the Pacific and Atlantic Oceans.*

Right: *Seen here cruising in the Atlantic, the USS Haddo (SSN-604) is one of 13 vessels in the Permit class of nuclear-powered attack submarines. The SSN-604 is capable of reaching a top speed of 20 knots on the surface and 30 knots submerged. Permits are able to operate at great depths and are very quiet. Armaments, including Mk 48 torpedoes and Harpoon missiles, are launched from four 21-inch tubes.*

Above: *The USS* Barbel *(SS-580) and her two sisters, the* Blueback *and* Bonefish, *all entered service at the end of the 1950s and are the last diesel-electric boats in the US Navy. Their design was advanced at the time – they introduced the Albacore teardrop hull into service. Speeds range from 23 knots on the surface to 25 knots submerged. They have six forward-firing 21-inch torpedo tubes for Mk 48 torpedoes.*

Overleaf: *The USS* Atlanta *(SSN-712) is one of the largest class of nuclear-powered attack submarines in service today. The Los Angeles class submarines displace 6900 tons submerged and, thanks to their single S6G reactor and two steam turbines, are able to achieve a maximum speed of over 30 knots. Both Harpoon and Tomahawk missiles can be launched by this class of vessel.*

Right: *The USS* Scamp *(SSN-588), one of the US Navy's Skipjack class nuclear-powered attack submarines. The* Scamp *and other vessels in the class are remarkable in many ways, not least because they were the first to combine nuclear propulsion and high speed. Indeed the design proved so successful that it was used as the basis for the early ballistic-missile submarines of the late 1950s and 1960s. The* Scamp *was decommissioned in 1987, after serving for 27 years.*

Above: *The USS* Minneapolis-Saint Paul
*(SSN-708) Los Angeles class submarine returns
to home waters. Built by General Dynamics in the
first half of the 1980s, her twin-geared turbines
develop 35,000shp, driving her at 30 knots
submerged. Her 6927-ton hull is 360 feet long
and has a diameter of 33 feet.*

Above: *The Soviet Victor class submarines first appeared in 1968, and 16 were completed over a period of seven years. Subsequent updates have led to the Victor II and III series. Victor IIIs have a displacement of 6300 tons and a speed of between 20 and 30 knots submerged. Six bow tubes are provided, two of 21-inch and four of 650mm caliber. Armament includes the SS-N-21 tube-launched cruise missile and the SS-N-16 anti-submarine missile.*

Left: *HMS* Repulse *is one of four Royal Navy ballistic nuclear submarines based on the US Navy's Lafayette class. The ships in this class are armed with 16 A-3 Polaris missiles and the associated Mk 118 fire-control system, and six 21-inch tubes for launching Mk 24 Tigerfish torpedoes. The navy's four Resolution class submarines have been in service since the late 1960s and will be replaced by the Vanguard class from 1992 onward.*

Above left: *The Royal Navy's most recent SSNs are the 5200-ton Trafalgar class, which started construction in 1977. Their powerplant is very similar to that of the earliest US SSNs, but only the* Trafalgar *itself (shown here) has a conventional seven-blade propeller. Armament is five 21-inch tubes firing a mix of Tigerfish wire-guided torpedoes and sub-Harpoon missiles.*

Above: *HMS* Tireless *is the third of the Royal Navy's Trafalgar class. Launched in July 1984, she was completed in October the following year. The fifth vessel in the class, HMS* Trenchant, *was commissioned in 1988, and when the seventh boat, HMS* Triumph, *goes to sea in 1991 production will switch to the more advanced W class powered by a new-generation PWR2 reactor.*

Above: *The Federal German Navy's U-26 (S-175)
heads home after a cruise. The U-26 was
completed by Rheinstaal Nordseewerke in 1975,
one of 18 Type 206 boats in service.
Displacement is 500 tons and these diesel-
electric boats are able to achieve speeds of 10
knots on the surface and 17 knots submerged.*

Above: *The West German U-19 (S-198) at sea. Armament consists of eight 21-inch tubes for up to 16 wire-guided torpedoes. Mines can be launched from an external carrier fitted to this particular type of coastal submarine, rather than being launched conventionally through the existing tubes as is the case with similar vessels in service in other navies.*

AIRCRAFT CARRIERS

Modern aircraft carriers fall into two distinct categories: huge strike carriers capable of operating the largest fixed-wing aircraft, and support carriers. Large carriers may be oil-fueled (CVs) or nuclear-powered (CVNs), but they both rely on catapults to launch aircraft, and some form of arresting gear to recover them. Because of their size and complexity CVs and CVNs are the most expensive warships in the world, and there are many critics who claim that they are no longer cost-effective. Against this naval aviators point out that a carrier battle group (CVBG) has an unmatched ability to deliver a massive weight of firepower on a potential enemy, while at the same time having all the flexibility of traditional naval power. Put another way, the US Navy's CVBGs are, apart from attack submarines, the only conventional means of taking the offensive against the Soviet Navy – all other forms of naval warfare are defensive.

The CVBG relies on the carrier's aircraft as the primary means of defense, forming an outer layer to intercept missile-carrying aircraft or ships before they can launch their weapons. The next layer is provided by long and medium-range missiles which back up the Combat Air Patrol (CAP). The innermost protective layer consists of short-range missiles providing 'point' defense (self-defense rather than 'area' defense). Any missiles which 'leak' through the point-defense layer are then dealt with by close-in weapons, the 20mm Phalanx 'gatling' gun firing 3000 rounds of depleted uranium per minute.

One of the critics' arguments, that the Soviet Navy was not building carriers, was confounded in 1984 by proof that the Soviets are building a 65,000-ton CVN at Nikolaiev. She and a sister will be at sea in the early 1990s, with another pair possibly joining them by the end of the decade. However, most other navies operate aircraft carriers in a supporting role, providing local air cover, surface strike capabilities and anti-submarine helicopter defense.

Despite the success of the British Sea Harrier Short TakeOff and Vertical Landing (STOVL) aircraft in the Falklands in 1982, supporters of conventional carriers point to the overwhelming advantages fixed-wing aircraft enjoy in performance and payload. The future may lie with STOVL, but not until performance and payload show considerable improvement. When that happens the design of big carriers may change dramatically, but for the present support carriers are a second-best alternative.

Critics of large carriers are apt to lose sight of the awesome firepower of a Carrier Air Group (CAG). A typical carrier has up to 90 aircraft, with sufficient fuel for two weeks of sustained operations. Not one aircraft carrier has been lost since 1945, compared to the large number of land bases lost to the United States by hostile military and political action. Carriers are not an alternative to land-based air power but they recognize that sea operations cannot be undertaken without local air superiority.

Right: *The nuclear carrier USS* Nimitz *(CVN-68), at 93,400 tons one of the largest warships ever built. At present the* Nimitz *carries a wing composed of 86 aircraft and helicopters. Defensive armament consists of close-in weapons – Sea Sparrow missiles and four Phalanx CIWS guns.*

Above: *A pair of Vought A-7 Crusader IIs on the flight deck of the USS* Nimitz. *By virtue of being nuclear-powered, the space saved on fuel for the carrier allows the vessel to carry 90 percent more aviation fuel for its air wing and 50 percent more ammunition.*

Above: *The first carrier to be built after World War II, the USS* Forrestal *(CV-59) was the lead-ship in a class of four. They have four side elevators and steam catapults, facilities essential for the optimum use of the 86-strong air wing on each carrier. Four steam turbines generate sufficient power for the ships to achieve a top speed of 34 knots.*

Previous pages: *The island superstructure of the USS* Franklin D Roosevelt *(CV-42) reveals the complexity of the modern fleet carrier. Although she was stricken in 1972, her sisters,* Midway *and* Coral Sea, *are still in service. All three vessels were designed in World War II but entered service too late to see action.*

Above: *The USS* Kitty Hawk *(CV-63) displaces 81,123 tons fully loaded and has an overall length of 1046 feet. Her four Westinghouse geared steam turbines and eight Babcock & Wilcox boilers generate 280,000shp, equivalent to a maximum speed of 32 knots. At an economical speed of 20 knots, the* Kitty Hawk *has an endurance of 8000 nautical miles.*

Above: *The USS* Kitty Hawk *underwent a Service Life Extension Program (SLEP) in 1988. As part of this modernization exercise, the ship's air wing was updated with its 20 A-7E Corsair IIs being replaced by 18 F/A-18 Hornets and a reduction in the number of F-14 Tomcats. Other aircraft on the carrier include EA-6B Prowlers, E-2C Hawkeyes, S-3A Vikings and Sea King helicopters.*

Overleaf: *The USS* Nimitz *can carry about 15,000 tons of aircraft-related stores but under intensive operational conditions the ship's supply of aviation fuel has to be replenished every 16 days. Despite the huge size of the carrier, no more than 40 percent of its aircraft can be accommodated below decks at any one time. The* Nimitz *was sent to join the Pacific Fleet after her 1987 refit which saw the extensive introduction of new radar systems.*

Previous page: *A stern-on view of the USS Midway (CV-41). The angled deck, when cleared for landing, allows aircraft to land well clear of the deck park of aircraft waiting to take off. Should the tailhook fail to 'take a wire' the pilot can safely take off again, with little risk of smashing into the deck park or safety barrier. Deck handlers preparing other aircraft for missions can also complete their work in comparative safety.*

Above: *A silver-suited firefighter stands by on the flight deck of the USS Coral Sea (CV-43). Red-shirted crewmen handle ordnance while other color designations indicate flight deck duties. For example, purple shirts are worn by refueling teams and hook-up men wear green shirts.*

Above: *Steam rises from a catapult at the forward end of the flight deck of the USS* Coral Sea *as an F/A-18 Hornet takes off. Within two seconds of the steam catapult being released, the aircraft accelerates to about 150 knots, sufficient speed to lift it clear of the carrier. The* Coral Sea *differs from her sister* Midway *in retaining three C11 Mod 1 steam catapults.*

Overleaf: *The* John F Kennedy (CV-67) *was built to the SCB 127C design between 1964 and 1966. A heavily modified version of the Kitty Hawk class, she has a distinctive angled uptake on the island superstructure to keep smoke away from the ship's electronic systems, and a different flight deck layout. With her automatic landing system she can operate aircraft in all weathers.*

Above: A Sea Sparrow missile is fired from one of the three Mk 29 launchers on the John F Kennedy. *Sea Sparrow is a point-defense missile credited with a range of 16,000 yards. Each eight-cell launcher is controlled by a Mk 91 radar tracker.*

Above right: *The* John F Kennedy *at speed in rough weather shows off her bow anchor. At full load a carrier tends to plow through waves rather than ride them, a situation that the US Navy seems willing to accept despite the risk of corrosion and occasional damage caused to aircraft.*

Right: *The US Navy had 428 F-14A Tomcat fighters in service in the late 1980s. They are highly agile interceptors capable of reaching Mach 2.3 and climbing to 60,000 feet. Armament includes a 20mm Vulcan cannon, two Phoenix, two Sparrow and two Sidewinder air-to-air missiles.*

Above: *The USS* Oriskany *(CV-34) was laid down
as the standard unit of the Essex class near the
end of World War II but was not completed until
September 1950. The four carriers in the class
are driven by four-shaft Westinghouse geared
steam turbines developing 150,000shp. When
new they could steam at 30 knots and had a
range of 18,000 miles at cruising speed.*

Above: *Four T-2B trainers fly over the USS* Lexington, *another survivor of the Essex class. The carrier first saw service in 1943, underwent large-scale modernization in the 1950s and remained in frontline service until 1968. As with all World War II US carriers, the Lexington's flight deck was made of 76mm-thick Douglas Fir planks, with horizontal armor confined to the hangar deck.*

Above: *The Soviet Navy's first step toward establishing carrier air power was the construction of the* Moskova *(seen here) and the* Leningrad *in the late 1960s. The air element of each ship comprises 14 Hormone helicopters. Armament is heavy, with two twin launchers for Goblet area-defense SAMs, two twin 57mm gun mountings, a twin launcher for anti-submarine SUW-N-1 missiles and two 12-barreled ASW rocket launchers.*

Above: The Kiev, *designated a large anti-submarine cruiser, first appeared in 1975. The ships in this class clearly have anti-submarine, sea-control and sea-denial roles. In addition to eight SS-N-12 Sandbox anti-ship missiles and a heavy defensive armament, the* Kiev *operates up to 13 Forger strike aircraft and up to 17 helicopters. Speed is estimated at 32 knots.*

Above left: *HMS* Ark Royal *entering Portsmouth, England, when first completed. She and her sisters are the world's largest gas turbine ships, with two-shaft Olympus turbines generating 112,000shp, equivalent to a speed of 28 knots. In the aftermath of the Falklands conflict, the Ark Royal was fitted with three close-in weapons systems.*

Left: *A later view of the* Ark Royal *showing the Phalanx CIWS guns and extended ski-jump. All three ships of the Invincible class will eventually receive the Dutch Goalkeeper CIWS in place of the Phalanx system. The* Ark Royal *operates an enlarged air group of eight FRS.1 Sea Harriers and 12 Sea King helicopters.*

Above: *The French Navy's* Clemenceau *was built between 1955 and 1961, and with her sister ship* Foch *she forms the backbone of France's naval aviation. Displacing 32,700 tons, she is driven by two-shaft geared steam turbines and has a top speed of 32 knots. In the mid-1980s she received two Crotale short-range missile systems to replace her four single 100mm guns.*

BATTLESHIPS

Few would have believed that the US Navy's surviving battleships would ever be re-commissioned. After all, the type of warfare for which they were designed, long-range action against other battleships with heavy-caliber guns, had been rendered obsolescent by the aircraft carrier. Yet there were influential forces at work. The US Marine Corps had been hostile to the decommissioning of the New Jersey (BB-62) in 1969, and the US Navy was also looking for ways to replace an aborted design, the nuclear strike cruiser (CGSN). This 17,000-ton vessel had been dropped because of runaway costs, and a proposal was put forward to provide equivalent firepower by rearming the four Iowa class battleships with Harpoon and Tomahawk missiles.

The rationale behind the project was to create four large missile-armed 'platforms,' each one to act as the flagship of a Surface Action Group (SAG). These would operate in conjunction with the navy's 15 Carrier Battle Groups, tying down and engaging Soviet surface forces which would otherwise be free to take offensive action against US and allied forces. The presence of a ship armed with 16 Harpoon anti-ship missiles and 32 Tomahawk cruise missiles would pose such a powerful threat that the Soviets could not ignore it. Should an amphibious assault be required, the SAG would provide gunfire support as a bonus, and new technology would almost certainly enhance the accuracy and lethality of the 16-inch guns.

Arguments about the vulnerability of large warships were countered by the provision of new electronic countermeasures, 20mm Phalanx 'gatlings' to shoot down missiles, and the protection afforded by powerful air-defense and anti-submarine escorts. Moreover, it is argued, the 12.1-inch armor belt, thick deck armor and minute compartmentation will protect the ship against several missile hits.

The New Jersey's first active assignment since Vietnam came in August 1983, when she went into the Caribbean as part of a show of force against Nicaragua. The following year she was ordered to the eastern Mediterranean to support American action against pro-Syrian factions in Lebanon. She carried out several bombardments against artillery positions firing on the US Marines in Beirut, the first time a US warship had fired her guns in anger in the Mediterranean for 40 years.

The survival of the four Iowas into the last quarter of the century is remarkable. Regarded once as white elephants, they have proved a better investment than their designers and builders could ever have dreamed. No other World War II vessels can boast such extended careers.

Right: The USS Missouri (BB-63) laid up in reserve. After overhaul and conversion, she and her sister ships now displace over 57,000 tons. Four sets of General Electric geared steam turbines drive them at 33 knots. An outstanding feature of the design is its phenomenal endurance: 5000 miles at 30 knots, a figure rising to nearly 15,000 miles at the more economical speed of 20 knots.

Above: *The USS* Iowa, *one of the most heavily armored vessels afloat. The main side belt is 307mm thick, tapering to 41mm, with extra protection up to 343mm thick abreast of the propeller shafts. The 16-inch turrets have 432mm of armor on the face, 184mm on the roof and 305mm at the rear.*

Right: *The design of the battleship's 16-inch triple turret dates from 1936 and requires a crew of 77 to function effectively. The guns operate at a rate of two rounds per minute, firing a 1226kg armor-piercing shell out to a range of 36,700 meters. The projectile can penetrate up to nine meters of reinforced concrete. Future developments include the provision of Search and Destroy Armor (SADARM) sub-munitions and extended-range shells.*

Above: *The* New Jersey *fires a full broadside against militia positions around the Lebanese capital Beirut on 9 January 1984. The eight armored box-launchers for her 32 Tomahawk cruise missiles can be seen amidships. The blast effect of a broadside, indicated by the flattening of the water on the starboard side, can inflict damage on the ship's deck fittings.*

Above right: *The two forward turrets of the* Iowa *firing during exercises. Two Phalanx CIWS flank the forward superstructure. These six-barreled 'gatlings' can destroy incoming anti-ship missiles by putting up a vast volume of fire – over 3000 depleted uranium slugs per minute. The ship is also protected by eight Mk 36 six-barreled chaff-launchers capable of decoying enemy missiles, and the latest electronic warfare systems.*

Right: *The Combat Engagement Station on the USS* Iowa, *with air and surface targets being plotted. Although parts of the battleship's radar and gunfire control systems are somewhat elderly, the communications systems are extremely modern, including the latest navigation aids such as WRN-5A and Omega satellite receivers.*

Right: *A broadside fired by the* Iowa *during exercises off Guantanamo Bay in the Caribbean. The* Iowa *differs in some details from the* New Jersey, *notably in the shape of her forward superstructure. The forward group of box-launchers for Tomahawk cruise missiles can be seen taking up the space formerly occupied by the two twin 5-inch gun mountings on either side. Four Phalanx CIWS are positioned on the corners at the top of the superstructure to provide overlapping fields of fire.*

Above: *Large-screen displays in the Combat Information Center of the cruiser USS Ticonderoga, a vessel that is a key element in a typical Surface Action Group that would accompany a single Iowa class battleship. With ships such as the Ticonderoga to provide close escort and information, the Iowa class ships will be much more formidable vessels.*

CRUISERS

The category of cruiser is something of an anomaly. Modern missile-armed ships bear little resemblance to the large gun-armed ships of late or post-World War II vintage. Yet several gun-armed cruisers survive, and it is hard to determine the dividing-line between missile-armed destroyers and missile-armed cruisers. The distinction is sometimes based on size, at other times it reflects capabilities. Perhaps the best definition of a modern cruiser is a warship equipped for two or more missions – air defense, surface combat and anti-submarine warfare.

The US Navy has no gun-armed cruisers in commission, although two of the Des Moines (CA-134) class remain in reserve. In contrast the Soviet Navy retains 11 Sverdlov class ships, built in the 1950s to a prewar Italian design. At least four of these are laid up in reserve but two serve as command ships. Like their contemporaries in other navies they are now expensive anomalies, requiring large crews and good for little beyond gunfire support. The Sverdlovs were only the first of three major cruiser programs initiated by the Soviet Union. During the first phase they planned to build 24 of the class as part of Stalin's Big Navy plans. The program was cut back by Khrushchev and 10 units were scrapped to make way for a new generation of high-technology missile-armed ships.

As the main role of American cruisers is to screen aircraft carriers, the advent of nuclear-powered carriers exposed the problems of operating oil-fired ships with nuclear-powered ones. The endurance of the escorts is measured in days, especially when the carrier battle group is steaming at high speed, whereas the nuclear-powered vessel can steam indefinitely at high speed. Out of this came the requirement for nuclear cruisers. The prototype, the *Long Beach* (CGN-9), was followed by two more in the 1960s, but series production did not start until a decade later. At one time it was hoped to build an all-nuclear surface navy, and in 1974 Congress even issued a directive promising that all units of future carrier battle groups would be nuclear-powered. But the staggering cost of such ships defeated the advocates of nuclear power, and no nuclear cruisers have been authorized since then.

In 1984 there were nine nuclear cruisers available to screen four nuclear carriers, a ratio of approximately two-to-one, but by the mid-1990s there will probably be no more than six or seven to screen six or seven carriers. To make up the numbers there will be an eventual total of 27 Aegis cruisers, conventionally powered but better equipped.

Right: *The USS* Mississippi, *one of the US Navy's four Virginia class nuclear-powered guided-missile cruisers, has a displacement of 11,300 tons when fully loaded and a length of 585 feet. Due to their cost and doubts about their precise maritime role, these four vessels are likely to be the last of their type in service.*

Above: *The USS* Virginia *(CGN-38) was the lead-ship of four nuclear-powered cruisers authorized in the first half of the 1970s. In the mid-1980s all four ships were modified with the removal of their helicopter hangars to make room for box-launchers for Tomahawk cruise missiles. Main armament comprises two quadruple Harpoon launchers, a 5-inch Mk 45 gun, two Standard SAM systems and ASROC anti-submarine missiles.*

Above: *The USS* Mississippi *(CGN-40) was built in the late 1970s and until the advent of the Aegis cruisers she and her sisters were the most effective anti-air warfare vessels in the world. As built they were equipped with Standard SM-1 missiles, now with a range of over 90 miles. The ship is not fitted for anti-submarine warfare, but for self-defense the* Mississippi *carries two sets of triple ASW torpedo launchers, one either side of the superstructure.*

Above: *The 10,500-ton cruiser* California *is dwarfed by the carrier* Dwight D Eisenhower, *but the carrier depends on the cruiser for intermediate-range air defense and protection against surface attack. The ship's main armament consists of Standard missiles (two 40-round magazines serving two single-arm Mk 13 launchers), a separate launcher for ASROC ASW missiles and a 5-inch Mk 45 gun. One quadruple set of Harpoon anti-ship missiles has been added to the after superstructure and the class will soon receive Tomahawk cruise missiles.*

Right: *A Standard SM-1 missile is launched from the forward Mk 13 launcher on the USS* California. *This ship is currently serving in the Atlantic, while her sister is on station in the Pacific. Both vessels will soon receive the New Threat Upgrade (NTU) modernization and will convert to the SM-2 version of the Standard missile.*

Above: *The USS* Bainbridge *(CGN-25) entered
service in the early 1960s and was upgraded in
the mid-1970s. Her obsolescent 3-inch guns
were replaced by two sets of quadruple Harpoon
anti-ship missiles, followed in the 1980s by two
Phalanx CIWS and the Standard SM-2(ER)
missile, a weapon with a range of 65 miles. Top
speed is 30 knots but the ship's reactors allow it
to stay on station for extended periods.*

Above: *The USS* Truxton *was originally meant to be a member of the conventionally-powered Belknap class of frigates but was given a nuclear powerplant before she joined the fleet as a cruiser in 1967. Thanks to recent improvements, it seems likely that this 8800-ton vessel will remain in service until the 1990s. She serves in the Pacific.*

Above: The USS Long Beach was the world's
first nuclear-powered surface ship when she
entered service in 1961. This 17,000-ton vessel
was originally designed to take Regulus II cruise
and Polaris intermediate-range ballistic missiles
but these were deleted before completion.
Alterations and a series of updates have changed
her considerably. Among the changes were the
removal of the radar arrays on the forward
superstructure and the addition of two Phalanx
CIWS guns.

Right: The Leahy (CG-16) is one of a class of nine
vessels armed with the Mk 2 Standard missile.
The two sets of twin 3-inch guns have been
removed since this photograph was taken and
replaced by Harpoon missiles and Phalanx CIWS.
Capable of reaching a top speed of 33 knots, the
Leahy has a range of 8000 miles at the more
economical speed of 14 knots.

Above: *Entering service in 1963, the USS* Harry E
Yarnell *(CG-17) was the second unit of the Leahy
class to be completed. The original design was a
radical departure from accepted conventions.
The adoption of a double 'mack' (combined mast
and stack) allowed the builders to keep the
superstructure compact. The ships were also
notable for their double-ended missile armament,
with two sets of launchers and trackers.*

Above: *The USS* Wainright *(CG-28) was the third ship of the Belknap class. Superficially similar to the Leahy class, they have a single 5-inch Mk 42 gun in place of the after Mk 10 missile launcher, as well as a helicopter hangar and flight deck to improve the ship's ASW capabilities. The* Wainright *was the trial ship for the SM-2(ER) version of the Standard SAM.*

Overleaf: *A view of the forward Mk 10 missile launcher on the USS* Home *(CG-30), one of nine Belknap class guided-missile cruisers serving with the US Navy. Five ships serve in the Pacific, four in the Atlantic.*

Above: *The USS* Sterett *(CG-31) was built by Puget Sound Naval Shipyard in the middle years of the 1960s. The ship has a displacement of 8065 tons fully loaded and is 547 feet long. Its two twin-shaft steam turbines generate sufficient power for the* Sterett *to reach a maximum speed of 33 knots.*

Above right: *The Aegis cruiser* Bunker Hill *(CG-52) is the sixth vessel in the Ticonderoga class. The design is an adaptation of the Spruance class destroyer, using the same hull. In all 27 ships are planned. Eleven are already in service. Two have been tested: the* Yorktown *against Libyan surface units in 1984 and the* Vincennes, *which shot down an Iranian airliner in 1988. Construction of the vessels occurs at yards in Maine and Mississippi.*

Right: *The USS* Josephus Daniels *(CG-27) in September 1985, displaying the improvements made to ships of the Belknap class, including the provision of Phalanx CIWS guns.*

Above: *The* Frunze *is the second of the Soviet Navy's Kirov class nuclear-powered cruisers. The role of these 28,000-ton vessels is unclear but their powerplant gives them virtually unlimited range. The main armament comprises 20 SS-N-19 anti-ship missiles with 96 SA-N-6 Grumble SAMs for defensive action. Cruising speed is 24 knots; top speed is 32 knots.*

Right: *A Kynda class vessel of the Soviet Navy with her forward quadruple SS-N-3B Shaddock anti-ship missile system clearly visible. This ship's powerplant is believed to be two-shaft geared steam turbines which can develop an estimated 100,000shp, sufficient for the ship to reach a top speed of 34 knots.*

Above: *A Kynda class cruiser refueling from an
oiler. The vessel's defensive armament includes a
twin-arm launcher for Goa medium-range SAMs
and two twin 76.2mm gun mountings. Amidships
there are two triple-barreled 533mm torpedo
tubes and on the forecastle there are two
RBU-6000 ASW rocket launchers. There are four
ships in the class – the* Groznyy, Admiral Fokin,
Admiral Golovko *and* Varyag *– all built between
1959 and 1965.*

Above: *The Kynda design has many unusual features including the two pyramid plated masts that carry Head Net-A search radars. Although a helicopter pad was provided on the fantail, it is rarely used and the vessel has no maintenance facilities for aircraft. Since 1981 the class has been updated with the addition of four six-barreled 30mm 'gatlings' and the installation of better radar systems.*

Above: The Slava *first appeared in 1982 and she
and the second ship of the Krasina class, the*
Marshal Ustinov, *are to be followed by the*
Chervona Ukraina *and at least one other unit.
The ship displaces an estimated 12,500 tons at
full load and two-shaft gas turbines give the ship
a top speed of 32 knots. Defensive weapons
include eight groups of SA-N-6 Grumble area-
defense SAMs in rotating vertical launchers.*

Above: *Several Kara class ships were built for the Soviet Navy between 1969 and 1980. The main armament comprises eight SS-N-14 Silex ASW missile launchers in two quadruple groups abreast of the forward superstructure. Other weapons include Goblet area-defense and Gecko point-defense missile systems, two twin 76.2 gun mountings, rocket launchers and 533mm torpedo tubes.*

Above, above right and right: *The 10 Kresta II
class ASW cruisers were developed from the
Kresta I design, but with SS-N-14 Silex missiles in
place of SS-N-3B Shaddock anti-ship missiles.
The hull is also considerably larger, as is the
displacement of 6200 tons. In addition to the
Silex missiles, the Kresta II class is defended by
Goblet area-defense missiles; each of the ship's
two magazines holds 20 rounds. A pair of twin
57mm gun mountings are situated amidships,
while four 30mm six-barreled 'gatlings' provide
close-in defense against missiles. Quintuple
533mm torpedo tubes are also positioned
amidships. ASW weapons include two
RBU-6000 and two RBU-1000 rocket launchers.
Steam turbines and boilers generate sufficient
power for the vessels to reach a top speed of 34
knots.*

DESTROYERS

As with cruisers, the earliest destroyers have only historic links with their modern counterparts. In theory destroyers are small, fast and cheap vessels, equipped to attack the enemy and to screen the main fleet. However, modern destroyers fitted to hunt submarines and to defend other ships against air attack are large and expensive. In fact the modern air-defense destroyer (DDG) is almost beyond the financial reach of most small navies. Attempts to build cheap destroyers have so far resulted in a number of under-capable warships.

By 1945 it was clear that torpedo attack against an enemy fleet was a thing of the past. After 1945 destroyer design advanced rapidly, with dual-purpose guns and radar-assisted fire control becoming commonplace, but it was clear that the medium-caliber guns of the day could not hope to destroy hostile aircraft before they could release their bombs or rockets. Guided missiles promised the requisite range and accuracy and by the mid-1950s several designs were in existence. By today's standards these beam-riding missiles were primitive but they established basic design principles.

As the need to attack an enemy fleet receded so did the need for a speed margin of seven or eight knots over ships such as carriers and cruisers. Instead the destroyer needed merely to be able to keep up with the ships it was escorting. Steam turbines, usually in a two-shaft arrangement, continued to be the standard powerplant until the 1960s, when gas turbine designs began to appear. At first the gas turbine was favored because it offered a good power-weight ratio, and pundits predicted that the size of warships would come down as a result. In practice the opposite happened. Gas turbines need vast quantities of air, necessitating large intakes and exhaust uptakes. Providing these, and exit routes for replacing defective turbines, led to the large superstructures seen in modern warships.

Current design philosophy stresses the need to decide the weapons to be carried before designing the hull, and so modern destroyers are much larger than their predecessors. The need to reduce radar signatures may counteract this trend, but today's big, spacious hulls are very seaworthy, comfortable and efficient, and it is unlikely that the major navies will go back to the cramped designs of old. Most current problems can be attributed to designers being forced to cram too much equipment into small hulls. The expensiveness of destroyers is the result of the high cost of modern weapons and electronics, not the price of steel.

Right: *The destroyer USS* Chandler *(DDG-996) on station in the Pacific, one of four Kidd class ships in service with the US Navy. These missile-armed ships are widely recognized as the best general-purpose destroyers in service with the fleet.*

Above: *After the Islamic Revolution in Iran, four modified Spruance class destroyers originally destined for the deposed Shah were taken over by the US Navy at a cost of 510 million dollars each. The four vessels in the class, the* Kidd *(the lead-ship), the* Callaghan, *the* Scott *and the* Chandler, *are similarly armed to the Spruance vessels, with Mk 26 missile launchers. The USS* Kidd *(shown here) joined the fleet in 1981 and recently saw service in the Persian Gulf.*

Above: *The USS* Scott, *like her sister ships, was designed with first-rate air conditioning and dust-exclusion systems for service under desert conditions. The Standard SM-2 missile is now being fitted, a process that got underway with the recommissioning of the* Scott *and the* Kidd. *The four ships of the class are to receive further upgrading including Harpoon anti-ship missiles. Phalanx CIWS guns have already been added and the ship's electronics have been overhauled.*

Above: *The USS* Davis *(DD-937) is one of the surviving Forrest Sherman class destroyers dating from the 1950s. She and five sisters were given a comprehensive ASW upgrade between 1967 and 1971 but all are now held in reserve, along with four unmodernized members of the class. As part of the upgrade program, the vessels were fitted with ASROC missiles and the SQS-35 variable depth sonar.*

Above right: *The USS* Spruance *(DD-963) was the first ship of the navy's largest post-1945 building program. Over 30 units had been completed by the 1980s. The basic design, incorporating a super-quiet hull large enough to accept new equipment without major refitting, was a great success. In service, the ships have proved extremely seaworthy, and widespread automation has cut down manpower requirements. Recent improvements have included the replacement of the ASROC launcher behind the forward 5-inch gun with a launch system for the Tomahawk cruise missile.*

Right: *The USS* Leftwich *(DD-984), along with other members of the Spruance class, has been given quadruple armored box-launchers for Tomahawk missiles, flanking the ASROC 'pepperbox' launcher on the forecastle. Each of the class now has eight Harpoon SSMs, placed athwartships at the back of the forward superstructure. Some of the class have received the SH-60B Seasprite LAMPS III helicopter to replace the original LAMPS I.*

Above: *The Soviet Navy's Kashin class ships were the world's first destroyers powered solely by gas turbines and came into service in the decade after 1962. In all 20 ships were built, divided between the Zhdanov yard in Leningrad and the 61 Kommuno yard on the Black Sea. Six Kashins were subsequently modernized and one, the* Provornyy, *was modified to test the SA-N-7 SAM system. The modified Kashin shown here has had her hull lengthened by two meters, with a helicopter pad and variable-depth sonar added aft. Other improvements include the addition of 'gatlings' for close-in defense and four SS-N2C Styx anti-ship missiles.*

Right: *The original Kashins had two Head Net-A (NATO designation) air-search radars, one on each mast, but many have subsequently had the second array replaced by the newer Big Net. The powerplant comprises four gas turbines, enabling the ships to reach a top speed of 36 knots. The main armament consists of two twin-armed launchers for SA-N-1 Goa surface-to-air missiles, twin 76.2mm gun mountings and a quintuple bank of 533mm torpedo tubes.*

Previous pages: *The USS* Paul F Foster *(DD-964), a member of the Spruance class.*

Above: *A modified Kashin class guided-missile destroyer in the Arabian Sea. Soviet warships have their hull numbers changed frequently, making identification difficult.*

Above right: *The* Otlichnyy *is the third of the Sovremennyy class destroyers. Developed from the Kresta hull, these ships are built by the Zhdanov yard in Leningrad; eight have been commissioned since 1981. Main armament comprises the SS-N-22 anti-ship missile, believed to have a range of about 120 miles. Air defense is provided by two SA-N-7 SAM systems, and two twin 533mm torpedo tubes are positioned amidships.*

Right: *The* Osmotritel'nyy *is the fourth vessel in the Sovremennyy class, completed in 1984 and sent to the Far East. The ship's twin 130mm gun mounting is a new model capable of firing 65 rounds per minute out to a maximum range of 28,000 meters. Air defense is provided by the SA-N-7 Gadfly missile, a system with a ceiling of about 15,000 meters. Each single-arm launcher has a reserve of 20 rounds located in a magazine below decks.*

Above: *The Royal Navy destroyer HMS Manchester maneuvers at speed off the Isle of Wight in 1986, the lead-ship of the Batch 3 Type 42 vessels. None of these ships saw service in the Falklands, but the lessons learnt in that conflict led to the ships receiving improved air defense weaponry, notably single 20mm and twin 30mm gun mountings. Phalanx CIWS were also bought from the United States and fitted as they became available. The* Manchester's *4.5-inch Mk 8 gun can fire up to 25 rounds per minute out to 23,000 meters.*

Above: *HMS* Manchester *was built by Vickers at Barrow-in-Furness, England, and was commissioned in 1982. Her three sister ships,* Gloucester, Edinburgh *and* York, *were commissioned in 1985. Being large ships the Batch 3s are likely to have an elaborate upgrade in due time. Eventually, it is hoped to equip them with a lightweight version of the Sea Wolf point-defense missile system. All ships will be modified to take the new Type 2050 low-frequency sonar as replacement for Types 184 and 2016.*

Left: *The Federal German Navy's* Hamburg *was the first of four destroyers completed in the mid-1960s for service in the Baltic against any high-level air threat. The armament of these somewhat dated vessels includes four MM-38 surface-to-surface missiles. For defense against low-level air attack each ship in the class carries four 40mm Breda-Bofors twin gun mountings.*

Above left: *The French destroyer* Dupleix *was the second of six Georges Leygues class ASW 'corvettes.' Main armament consists of four MM-38 Exocet anti-ship missiles, backed up by a 100mm dual-purpose gun and a Crotale point-defense SAM system. ASW sensors include a large DUBV-26 bow sonar and a DUBV-43 variable-depth sonar placed aft. Extra firepower is provided by L5 ASW torpedo tubes.*

Above: *The Canadian destroyer* Iroquois *(DDH-280) is one of four helicopter-carrying destroyers completed in the early 1970s. Setting new standards in ASW capability, each ship carries two Sea King helicopters. The vessels are currently undergoing modernization. During this process they will receive a Mk 41 vertical-launch system for the Standard SM-2 SAM, a 76mm replacement for the existing 5-inch gun and a Mk 15 Phalanx close-in weapons system.*

Above: *HMAS* Brisbane, *one of three guided-
missile destroyers bought from the US Navy by
the Australians in the 1960s. Essentially members
of the Charles F Adams class, these ships have
been slightly modified to take the Ikara missile
system. Despite their relatively small
displacement (4500 tons), these anti-air warfare
vessels are well armed; their weapons systems
include an aft-mounted Tartar SAM launcher, an
ASROC system positioned amidships and a
forward-mounted 5-inch dual-purpose gun.*

Above: *A side-on view of HMAS* Perth. *In the mid-1970s this ship and its sisters underwent a modernization program that include the fitting of Standard SM-1A missiles; a decade later their launch systems were modified to fire Harpoon SSMs. The powerplant, steam turbines and superheated boilers, delivers 70,000shp, allowing the vessels to reach a top speed of 35 knots.*

FRIGATES

Modern frigates are subject to the same design tendencies as bigger ships in that they are growing in size and complexity. Even the single ASW mission is now so demanding that ships of 5000 tons are common. The major problem in designing a modern ASW frigate is the sheer volume of information which must be handled: an escort can be swamped with inputs from fixed seabed sensors, sono-buoys dropped by aircraft, dipping sonar contacts from helicopters and even contacts gained by friendly submarines. The processing of this volume of information rapidly and accurately calls for large computer capacity, dozens of display units and excellent communications equipment. Formerly, escorts were only at risk from submarine torpedoes but now they can be attacked by both subsurface-launched and air-launched missiles, so they must be equipped with expensive anti-missile systems. The net result is a rising spiral of costs and a decline in the number of frigates which can be built. With the Soviet submarine fleet expanding steadily there is understandable alarm in NATO and the Western Alliance.

One proposed cure is for the NATO navies to achieve economies of scale by designing and building a standardized vessel. The NATO Frigate for 1990 (NFR-90) project is well advanced, with nine countries participating in the project, but narrow national interests could still wreck the program. The project has been carefully structured to ensure that all participants share not only the costs but also the industrial benefits equitably, while also guaranteeing that each navy ends up with a capable warship at the right price. If it fulfills its present promise the NFR-90 could be the biggest series order outside the United States since World War II.

The US Navy has some 90 frigates in active commission, and nine assigned to the Naval Reserve Force, with joint active-reservist crews. As part of the 600-ship force planned by the Reagan administration the number required is 101, with eight frigates assigned to amphibious groups, 63 to defend military convoys, and 30 to escort underway replenishment groups. However, as funding for a 600-ship navy begins to run out the likelihood of more frigates entering service is becoming more remote. Apart from the small number of NFR-90s likely to be ordered (the minimum needed to secure American industrial participation in the program) new purchases are unlikely until well into the 1990s.

In Europe the same difficulties have arisen, but on a smaller scale. The Royal Navy tried to keep the cost of its new Type 23 down, but the complex demands of ASW in the 1990s forced the price up before the lead-ship was even ordered. Elsewhere, Australia and New Zealand are hammering out a joint ANZAC design, but political objections have complicated the process. High technology has not come to the rescue. Plans for Surface Effect frigates and SWATH hulls abound, but a practical alternative to the traditional monohull has yet to appear.

Right: HMS Broadsword, *first of the Royal Navy's Type 22 frigates, proved herself in action in the Falklands campaign of 1982.*

Above: *The USS* Antrim *(FFG-20) was commissioned in September 1981, the twelfth in the Oliver Hazard Perry class. These ships, a total of 51 units, were ordered between 1973 and 1984. Design specifications emphasized modular construction permitting a ship capable of being built in large numbers during an emergency. Every attempt was made to control costs, to the extent of eliminating one power shaft. To compensate for the consequent loss of maneuverability, two retractable auxiliary propulsion pods were provided.*

Right: The Robert G Bradley *(FFG-49), built by the Bath Ironworks, Maine, was commissioned in August 1984. The vessel carries 36 Standard SM-1 SAMs and four Harpoon SSMs, all fired from a single-arm Mk 13 launcher on the forecastle. The ship is also armed with a single 3-inch Mk 75 gun, Mk 15 Phalanx CIWS and triple Mk 32 ASW torpedo launchers. The large aft hangar accommodates a pair of SH-60B Seahawk LAMPS III helicopters.*

Above: *The USS* Brooke, *lead-ship in a class of guided-missile frigates, fires an ASROC anti-submarine missile during a simulated attack on the USS* Bluegill. *The ships of the Brooke class have a displacement of 3245 tons fully loaded and a top speed of 27 knots. Their armament includes one Mk 22 launcher and one eight-tube ASROC launcher.*

Above: *The USS* Marvin Shields *(FF-1066) turns at speed while on patrol. One of 46 Knox class frigates, the* Marvin Shields *was originally fitted with Mk 25 Sea Sparrow launchers for close-in anti-aircraft defense, but these were later replaced by a single Mk 15 Phalanx CIWS gun. The hull is equipped with anti-roll fin stabilizers.*

Above: *US Navy personnel inspect the damage inflicted on the USS* Stark *by two French-made AM-39 Exocet missiles fired by Iraqi Mirages during the Gulf War. Although the frigate's design has come in for criticism, the comparatively light damage suffered by the* Stark *suggests that its armor, a mixture of alloy, steel and Kevlar, helped to minimize the scale of destruction. The ship's company also proved that their damage-control procedures were excellent.*

Above: *The USS* Stark *in happier times. The enquiry into the Exocet attack revealed that the command team in the Combat Information Center (CIC) did not initiate the correct defensive measures when the Iraqi Mirages attacked. Consequently the ship's electronic countermeasures did not jam the Exocets, nor did the Phalanx CIWS open fire.*

Above: *The USS* Knox *(FF-1052) was the lead-ship of a class of 46 destroyer escorts built between 1965 and 1974. Some of the class, including the* Knox, *were fitted with a light bulwark and a spray-deflecting strake. Other improvements on the basic design include the addition of Harpoon missiles and the replacement of the Sea Sparrow point-defense SAM system by a Mk 15 Phalanx CIWS. The original DASH hangar was enlarged to accommodate the SH-2F Seasprite LAMPS I helicopter.*

Right: *The ASROC 'pepperbox' fitted to ships of the Knox class has been modified to permit Harpoon anti-ship missiles to be fired from the left-hand pair of cells. Two additional Harpoons are carried in a magazine below the bridge. Here, a Harpoon missile leaves the ASROC launcher on the USS* Badger *(FF-1071).*

Left: *The USS* O'Callahan *(FF-1051) is a unit of the Garcia class. Built in the 1960s, they are now considered obsolescent, and after decommissioning, they were offered to Pakistan. The design did have several advanced features when it was introduced into service, notably its vertical turbo-pressurized boilers.*

Above left: *The USS* Bowen *(FF-1079) shows off her bow strake and bulwark as she steams through a light swell. She has been re-armed with the Mk 15 Phalanx CIWS. Like the other members of the Knox class, the Badger was re-designated as a frigate in the mid-1970s.*

Above: *The USS* Bronstein *(FF-1037) and the USS* McCloy *(FF-1038) were built in the early 1960s but proved to be too slow to be effective ASW escorts. They were, however, the last frigates to be armed with 3-inch guns. Some years ago the McCloy hit the headlines when her towed array sonar system became entangled with a Soviet Victor III nuclear attack submarine.*

Above left and left: *The USS* Glover *(FF-1098) was built by the Bath Ironworks, Maine, between 1963 and 1965. Her hull is identical in design to the Garcia class, but she was given a pumpjet propulsor and the after 5-inch gun was removed to increase accommodation and laboratory facilities. The Glover's stern was raised during the trials of the SQS-35 variable-depth sonar. The vessel now carries out regular operational cruises with the US Atlantic Fleet.*

Above: *The Soviet Navy does not have anything like the range of escort designs of the US Navy, but their equivalent of the Western frigate is the Krivak series of 3500-ton escorts. The Druzhnyy (seen here) is a Krivak I, armed with four SS-N-14 Silex ASW missiles, a pair of SA-N-4 Gecko point-defense missiles, two quadruple 533mm torpedo tubes and two twin 76.2mm gun mountings. The tenth of 21 units, the Druzhnyy was built by the Zhdanov yard in Leningrad.*

114

Left: *Similar to the Petya class are the numerous Grishas. Despite being about the same displacement (1100 tons), they are, however, designated as small anti-submarine ships. This Grisha III is fitted with a 20-round SA-N-4 Gecko point-defense system, a twin 57mm gun mounting, a 30mm 'gatling,' two RDU-6000 ASW rocket launchers and two twin 533mm torpedo tubes.*

Above left: *The Soviet Navy operates several light frigates rated as SKRs (patrol ships). This unidentified Petya II carries two twin 76.2mm gun mountings, four RBU-2500 ASW rocket launchers and five quintuple 400mm torpedo tubes. The class came into service in the early 1960s and after a quarter of a century in service it seems likely that some units have been placed in reserve.*

Above: *HMS Cornwall is the first of four frigates ordered to replace vessels sunk in the Falklands. Based on the hull of the Batch 2 Type 22, the Boxer class, these ships have been fitted with a less specialized armament, including Harpoon missiles and a pair of Sea Wolf point-defense systems. Other weaponry includes a 4.5-inch gun and triple ASW torpedo launchers. The Cornwall class vessels have a new lightweight Type 911 tracking system and an upgraded surveillance radar.*

Above: HMS Brilliant *was the third of the Royal Navy's Type 22 Broadsword class frigates. Commissioned in April 1981, she saw service during the Falklands conflict the following year. The primary role of the Type 22 is mid-ocean ASW, and the design consequently emphasized a high degree of seakeeping. The ship's Sea Wolf system provides point-defense against air attack but its main purpose is to defend against 'pop-up' missiles fired by submarines such as the Soviet Charlie class.*

Above right: *The French* aviso Commandant Blaison *was the thirteenth of the d'Estienne d'Orves class and was built at Lorient between 1979 and 1982. These coastal escorts have proved to be very economical to operate and highly seaworthy. A total of 17 such vessels were built from 1972 to 1984.*

Right: *The* Second Maitre le Bihan *was the eighth unit of the d'Estienne d'Orves class to enter service. She is armed with a single 100mm gun and a 375mm ASW rocket launcher. Unlike the Commandant Blaison, she is not armed with MM-38 Exocet missiles. The vessel's powerplant comprises two-shaft diesels to provide a maximum speed of 23½ knots.*

Above: *The Federal German Navy's Type 122
frigate* Bremen *was the lead-ship of six vessels
ordered in 1977 and completed in 1984. In
general the Bremen class ships resemble the
Dutch Kortenaer design on which they are based.
Armament, including Harpoon missiles, Sea
Sparrow SAMs and a 76mm OTO-Melara dual-
purpose gun, is very similar, but there are
numerous differences in electronics and
machinery.*

Above: *The Italian frigate* Maestrale *was built by Cantieri Navali Riuniti between 1978 and 1982, one of a class of eight vessels. The armament is impressive for a 3000-ton hull: four Otomat Mk 2 SSMs are positioned on the after deckhouse, with an Albatross point-defense SAM system and a 5-inch gun forward. Other weapons include twin 40mm Breda Compact guns mounted amidships and triple ASW torpedo tubes.*

AMPHIBIOUS ASSAULT SHIPS

Amphibious landings are almost as old as naval history itself, but modern techniques and ships owe much to the experiences gained by the vast amphibious fleets that saw service during World War II. Today, many navies maintain amphibious forces but the greatest practitioner of the art is the US Navy. Strategic mobility is a major requirement of all three arms of the US military, all of which dedicate some of their forces to overseas deployment. For the US Navy this takes the form of amphibious vessels able to facilitate the movement of the Marine Corps and vessels to keep units of the army and air force supplied with fuel and stores wherever they are stationed.

To put the Marine Corps ashore the navy maintains what are without doubt the best-equipped and most elaborate amphibious forces in the world. Currently there are 45 ships in active commission, and two tank landing ships operated by the Naval Reserve Force. Some 15 to 20 percent of these are in various stages of refit and overhaul at any one time. The remainder are divided roughly in equal numbers between the Atlantic, Pacific and Indian Oceans and the Mediterranean. One of the eight US amphibious squadrons (PHIBRONs) is normally deployed in the Mediterranean, a second in the western Pacific, and a third operates periodically in the Caribbean.

Existing amphibious warship types can be divided into six groups: amphibious assault ships, dock landing ships, major tank landing ships, minor landing craft, transports, and command ships. The age of many of the older ships has been of growing concern to the US military establishment for many years.

Modern coast defenses, especially surveillance systems and such refinements as mobile missile batteries, make the traditional direct assault a very risky operation. A fleet lying off a well-protected landing beach would suffer intolerable losses. The answer lies in the Air Cushion Landing Craft (LCAC), whose high approach speed allows the amphibious troops to disembark from their transports over the horizon, outside the range of shore-based weapons.

Much is made of the Soviet amphibious capability but there is no sign of anything like the US Navy's commitment to power projection. Although there has been some investment in military air cushion vehicles, only two landing ships with docks have been built and only small numbers of tank landing craft and ships. Nor has the naval infantry undergone any noticeable expansion commensurate with any intention to match American amphibious capabilities.

Right: *Soft-skinned vehicles descend the 112-foot ramp of a Newport tank landing ship, one of the 20 vessels in the class. With a top speed of 20 knots the Newports are able to keep up with amphibious assault groups, and their armament, two Mk 15 Phalanx CIWS, gives them a measure of protection from missile attack. A typical combat load could consist of 430 troops or 500 tons of cargo.*

Above: *The USS* Blue Ridge *(LCC-19) was specifically designed for a command role in any amphibious operation. Fitted with two eight-tube Mk 25 Sea Sparrow missile launchers and four 3-inch Mk 22 guns, these vessels also carry highly modern radar suites and satellite communications. Top speed is 21½ knots, the power generated by a single steam turbine.*

Above right: *A CH-46 helicopter delivers stores to the aft pad of an amphibious assault vessel. These helicopters are often stationed on Iwo Jima class ships with a cruising range of up to 10,000 miles.*

Right: *The amphibious transport USS* Nashville, *one of 15 vessels in the Austin class. The Austin ships can carry up to 930 troops and have about 15,700 square feet of cargo space. Each ship's docking well can accommodate a variety of assault craft. The ships can take up to six Sea Knight helicopters but only for a limited time.*

Above: *The unusual configuration of the USS Saginaw arises from the need to steam at 20 knots. The traditional bow ramp and square doors were not compatible with high speeds, so the designers gave the Newport class a forward ramp allowing vehicles on to the ship without reducing its seaworthiness or speed.*